Highway to Wholeness

Overcoming Abuse God's Way
Rags to Riches

Study Guide
Workbook

WRITTEN BY

Charlana Kelly

Highway to Wholeness

Cover design by Wendy Wittulski of CHiCPEA Studio 352-208-2941

A SpeakTruth Media Book
PO Box 1448, Crockett TX 75835 | Voice or Text: 936-222-8918

ISBN: 978-0-9985190-5-0

DEDICATION

This Workbook is dedicated to every person whose heart was/is broken by abuse.

May God our Father, Jesus our Healer and Holy Spirit our Comforter give you revelation of His unfailing and unending love and acceptance, so you too can live the abundant life that Jesus died to give.

To God be all the glory, forever and ever!

Contents

Introduction

This workbook is an accompaniment to the book, *Overcoming Abuse God's Way Rags to Riches* written by Janet Marie Napper and Brenda Branson. As you read each section spend time allowing the Holy Spirit to dig deep into your heart. God desires complete deliverance, healing, and restoration—spirit, soul, body. This restoration includes your mind, will, and emotions. He is working in your heart to create a whole and beautiful person. A replica of Jesus Christ with unique expressions of His character and love.

Take your time with each section, consider the Scriptures, questions, and prayers. It's okay, even preferred that you spend a week at a time with each topic to allow a deep work in your heart. Meditate on the Scriptures and repeat the prayers often. Your breakthrough will come. As you keep following God's ways, you will be healed of every hurt and every hindrance will be removed. You will be set free to walk with and love your Lord and Father beyond reason. This is His grand plan for you as His child, precious jewel, and eternal companion.

God has provided a way, a safe way, a beautiful way. A way that leads to life. Not as you have known it up to now, but a life He has provided for you that will last throughout eternity. The perfect, pure God kind of life called *Zoe*. A complete and full life in union with Christ and relationship with your Creator. Nothing missing nothing broken!

This is the *Highway of Wholeness!* As you move closer and closer to Him, you are being purified as His radiant Bride, full of His splendor and glory.

Don't worry or fear if you are not perfect, He is not looking for perfection, but a heart that is loyal to Him. As you remain faithful, His work in you will be so gently and beautifully brought to completion. You are His masterpiece; His living love poem being told to a lost and hurting world. It's His inner work in your heart that finishes the transformation. Your part is only to choose His life daily and purpose your heart to follow His Word by surrendering to His loving ways.

Know this, YOU are loved and prayed for daily as you journey with Him through this Workbook. One thing is for sure, your life will never be the same again as you stay steady in your pursuit of the God of all Creation. He created you for a blessing. He is your Heavenly Father and your Lord Jesus Who both love you beyond reason.

"I pray with great faith for you, because I'm fully convinced that the One who began this glorious work in you will faithfully continue the process of maturing you and will put his finishing touches to it until the unveiling of our Lord Jesus Christ!" The Apostle Paul in Philippians 1:6, TPT.

Before you begin this journey, let's make sure your life in Christ is settled. Everything you will experience and learn begins with a relationship with your Jesus. Heaven is a real place and there's only one way to get there. Faith in Jesus Christ! Life can deal some harsh blows. But Jesus told us, it's the thief who comes to steal, kill and destroy. He came so that all who receive Him can have an abundant life (John 10:10). To receive this life Jesus came to give you, or to renew your faith in Him, all you need to do is pray. Repent of your sins, ask Jesus to come into your heart, and receive His forgiveness. Then you can know that your future in heaven is settled this day. Let's pray,

Father, in the mighty name of Jesus, I humbly repent of my sins, receive Your forgiveness and open my heart to receive Jesus as my Savior and Lord. I surrender my life to Him, fulfill all Your will in my life and fill me with the Holy Spirit. I rejoice that my name is written in the Lamb's Book of Life and that I will spend eternity with You in Heaven. Teach me, lead me, and guide me in Your ways of righteousness from this day forward and forever. In Jesus' name, I pray. Amen.

Be sure to keep a journal with you as you go through this Workbook to write extra notes and prayers along the way. Now let's get started as we walk the *Highway of Wholeness* together.

You Will Live and Not Die

"I will not die; instead, I will live

to tell what the Lord has done." — Psalm 118:17

Like Janet, we have all been through seasons and life experiences that left us feeling alone, hopeless, and unloved. As strong as the human spirit is, these moments leave deep wounds in our heart that can shape our view of ourselves and every person in our life. Our perceptions and expectations become perverted, leaving us vulnerable and helpless. Often, we find ourselves fighting for what we so desperately need. In our desperation, we try to control everything and everyone around us for fear of losing again. The problem is that we end up losing the very things we tried to hold on to.

It's time to be free from desperation and hopelessness. You are alive because God has a plan for your life. He wants to be the source and sufficiency for everything you need, want, or dream of having. First, you need to let go of the past, release it, forgive and let go.

Briefly list the moments when you felt alone, hopeless, and unloved; perhaps like you were left to die. Also, note the person who made you feel those emotions.

_____

_____

_____

_____

Think of the ways you tried to earn their love or manipulate them to get what you needed. List those ways here. Did you get what you needed from them?

_____

_____

_____

_____

Consciously decide right now to forgive them and let them go. Forgive yourself too. Let's pray.

Father, I choose to forgive myself and them. I let go, I release it all now in Jesus' name, Amen.

Receive His love and forgiveness.

Read these verses;

"So be strong and courageous! Do not be afraid and do not panic before them. For the LORD your God will personally go ahead of you. He will neither fail you nor abandon you." Deuteronomy 31:6

"... for God has said: "Never will I leave you, never will I forsake you." Hebrews 13:5b

"For I know the plans I have for you," says the LORD. "They are plans for good and not for disaster, to give you a future and a hope." Jeremiah 29:11, NLT

"... those who hope in me will not be disappointed." Isaiah 49:23 (end of verse)

"To those who were rejected and not my people, I will say to them: 'You are mine.' And to those who were unloved, I will say: 'You are my darling.'" Romans 9:25, TPT

"You, Lord, are forgiving and good, abounding in love to all who call to you." Psalm 86:5

Now, think about those feelings of being alone, hopeless, and unloved. Were you really alone, or was God with you? Were you without hope? Were you unloved? How does it make you feel differently to know that you are not alone, there is hope for you in Christ, and you are loved?

_____

_____

_____

_____

Sit silently for a few minutes and thank God for His unconditional love, thank Him that He will never leave you alone. Thank Him for sending Jesus for you, thank Him that He will not disappoint you as you continue to hope in Him. Let His presence flood your soul.

Make this declaration;

I will live and tell everyone
about how good my Lord has been to me.

What is one life lesson you can take away from what you've learned in this section? How will you apply it in your life right now?

_____

_____

_____

_____

Additional Notes

You are Loved Beyond Measure

"There is a God-shaped vacuum in the heart of each man which cannot be satisfied by any created thing but only by God the Creator, made known through Jesus Christ." – Blaise Pascal

The only love that will satisfy your heart is the *agape*, unconditional love of God. Yes, like Janet, we love our mother, father, siblings, friends, caretakers, guardians, and even random strangers along our path. They love us too, but the love we share together is conditional, based on performance. This is why with all of Janet's efforts to feel loved, each one fell short keeping her in a place of pain.

When we are weak emotionally, and in need of praise and approval from people, we will look for love in all the wrong places. This ends with disappointment and a perpetual wound filled with old feelings of being unloved. Listen, even the best marriages and friendships let us down because we are not perfect. The only perfect love is God's love, a love that only He can give. A love that He has put in your heart. A love that you must acknowledge to receive the benefit of.

Once we have a revelation of God's love and who we are in Christ, we stop chasing after the inadequate love of people and become satisfied and content to live in the agape love of our Creator. It's a choice to receive, celebrate, and live in God's love.

Identity plays a key role here. If you find your identity in people, then you will never feel loved. However, when you find and walk in the identity God has given you, then you find peace, joy, and contentment in His love. And, you can begin to love others with the same love you have received from Him. Rest in the arms of your loving Father, Who chose you and approves of you. Step-by-step begin to accept who you are in Him and believe you are exactly who He says you are.

Let's begin by identifying and rooting out the lies you have believed about yourself. List them here. If you need more space write a list in your journal.

_____

_____

_____

_____

Here are some common lies we all tend to believe;

- I am bad
- I am unworthy

- I am broken
- Everyone hates me
- Things will never go well for me
- I can't, or I will never change

Ask for Heavenly help... *Holy Spirit reveal and help me root out every lie I have believed about myself.*

Read these verses;

"Yet God has made everything beautiful for its own time. He has planted eternity in the human heart..." Ecclesiastes 3:11a, NLT

"And this hope is not a disappointing fantasy, because we can now experience the endless love of God cascading into our hearts through the Holy Spirit who lives in us!" Romans 5:5, TPT

"God decided in advance to adopt us into his own family by bringing us to himself through Jesus Christ. This is what he wanted to do, and it gave him great pleasure." Ephesians 1:5, NLT

Now, let's replace those lies with truth. Read each one of these statements as though God is speaking directly to you. Pause after each sentence letting it sink into your heart. Then, thank God for the truth taking root, becoming a reality in your life, and shaping what you believe about yourself.

- You are never outside My reach.
- The world rejected you, the enemy wanted to destroy you, but I never took My eyes off you.
- In fact, you are the apple of My eye.
- I formed you in your mother's womb. I knew you. Before you were born, I set you apart, called you My very own.
- You were not an afterthought.
- I am not mad at you, I am mad about you.
- I accept you. You are beautiful, you are loved beyond reason.
- You cannot change My mind about you.
- I chose you. You are spoken for, you are Mine.
- When you find yourself smack dab in the middle of your mess or sin and the world says, "We don't have time for you." I have all the time in the world for you. I have an eternity of blessing planned for you.
- I created you for My glory. You are My prized possession.
- You are not defined by what you do for me, but what I did for you.
- Your name is written on My hands, I cannot forget you.
- You don't need to try to earn My love, I have already given it to you in full without condition.
- You are never separated from My love, no matter what you say or do. I am with you and for you.

- I rejoice over you with singing.

- You are My treasure.

- I long to take care of everything you need. I am your Provider.

- If you were the only sinner on earth, I would have still died for you so that we could be together throughout eternity.

- You are My darling. I AM in love with you.

Commit this verse to memory and start doing it,

Philippians 4:8; *"So keep your thoughts continually fixed on all that is authentic and real, honorable and admirable, beautiful and respectful, pure and holy, merciful and kind. And fasten your thoughts on every glorious work of God, praising him always."* *TPT*

What is one life lesson you can take away from what you've learned in this section? How will you apply it in your life right now?

_____

_____

_____

_____

Beauty FOR ASHES, *Joy* FOR MOURNING, *Strength* FOR FEAR, *Double Honor* FOR SHAME

"Evil comes from the abuse of free will." – C. S. Lewis

Perhaps you, like Janet, have lived through a nightmare. It's so beautiful that she came to a place of forgiveness and love as she came to terms with the truth about her Creator and her abusers. It's time for you to come to terms with the fact that you did nothing to cause the abuse you have suffered. You did not invite it or cause it, nor do you need to be ashamed of it.

As a minister, people often ask me, "If God loves me so much, why did He allow me to be abused?" My answer is simple, "We live in a fallen world, where men and women choose wrong over right, evil over good, hate over love, and fear over faith." What they don't consider is the damage their choices do to the innocent victim.

Settle it right now, God did not choose you to be abused. He does not want you to live in silent shame and fear. Jesus came to set you free from every fear and shame. He wants you to release it all to Him. Start by telling Him what happened to you. He already knows but He wants you to come to Him as your Father. He wants to have a beautiful relationship of sharing and caring with you. He wants you to depend on Him by making Him the most important person in your life. Tell Him everything, ask Him everything.

Write down the things you can think of that you need to release to the Lord. This includes worry, doubt, anger, fear, shame, guilt and pain.

_____

_____

_____

_____

Read these verses;

"Anxiety in a man's heart weighs him down, but a good word makes him glad." Proverbs 12:25

"Cast all your anxiety on him because he cares for you." 1 Peter 5:7

Jesus came, "To console those who mourn in Zion, to give them beauty for ashes, the oil of joy for mourning, the garment of praise for the spirit of heaviness; That they may be called trees of righteousness, the planting of the Lord, that He may be glorified." Isaiah 61:3

"Instead of your shame you shall have double honor, and instead of confusion, they shall rejoice in their portion.

Therefore, in their land they shall possess double; everlasting joy shall be theirs." Isaiah 61:7

"For God has not given you a spirit of fear, but of love, and power, and a sound mind." 2 Timothy 1:7

"If you continue in My Word you are My disciples, you will know the truth and the truth will make you free. If the Son sets you free, you are free indeed." John 8:32 & 36

List the promises God made to you in these verses.

_____

_____

_____

_____

Say this, "By *faith,* I receive His promises right now. *I am beautiful, I am joyful, I will praise my Father and Lord all day long. I am free from shame and guilt."*

Pray this;

Father, I release my feelings of guilt and shame to You. Thank You that You want to make me free from both. I resist all fear right now and receive Your spirit of love, power, and a sound mind. I thank You for healing me from every wound and all the pain I've endured. Fill me with joy

as I praise You for all the good You are bringing into my life.
Create in me a clean heart and a steadfast spirit so I can serve
you every day for the rest of my life. I thank You I am free,
free from sin, sickness, and death. I cast every care, doubt,
and worry upon You and trust You with all my days. I release
anger and thank You for defending me and restoring me and
fulfilling all Your will in my life. I love You Father. Holy
Spirit continue to help me every day. In Jesus' name, Amen!

What is one life lesson you can take away from what you've learned in this section? How will you apply it in your life right now?

Additional Notes

When You Search You Find

"How beautiful are the feet of those who bring Good News!"

– Romans 10:15b

When God created the family, it was His intention that the father and mother would be a picture of His goodness and blessing in the home as both raised their children in the nurture and love that God Himself had for them. As parents fulfill this God-given purpose, children grow up in an atmosphere of love, acceptance, and safety helping them to grow strong in their identity and purpose.

Many children like Janet, and perhaps you, don't have the benefit of God's intentions because their parents or guardians did not provide a Christ-centered home life. This causes children to search for anyone to provide for their needs, especially the love and acceptance they deeply desire.

Unfortunately, in the world, there is no one who can provide for you what either God or God-fearing (reverent) people can give. Often the world only wants what it can get from you. As soon as you become useless to them, they will discard you without an ounce of concern for your wellbeing.

As you keep searching, God keeps sending people who point you in the right direction. Eventually, you find the truth. You find Him, and you find out like Janet, everything you wanted, hoped, and dreamed about had already been provided for you. It's a simple shift, a change of focus, turning from the world to Christ and looking to Him to fulfill all your needs. And... He does!

Name some of the people God has sent to you, who have shared truth with you and loved you with His unconditional love.

_____

_____

_____

_____

Write down how it makes you feel to know the Creator of the Universe is sending people to help you, even rescue you from bad situations.

_____

_____

Say the following statement three times with intention and faith, notice how you feel on the inside each time you say it;

I am special, I am loved, I have been rescued, I am healed, I am delivered, I am restored by Jesus.

Read and meditate on these verses;

"For I know the plans I have for you," says the Lord. "They are plans for good and not for disaster, to give you a future and a hope ... when you pray, I will listen. If you look for me wholeheartedly, you will find me." Jeremiah 29:11— 13

Jesus said, "And so I tell you, keep on asking, and you will receive what you ask for. Keep on seeking, and you will find. Keep on knocking, and the door will be opened to you." Luke 11:9

"Everything we could ever need for life and complete devotion[a] to God has already been deposited in us by his divine power. For all this was lavished upon us through the rich experience of knowing him who has called us by name

and invited us to come to him through a glorious manifestation of his goodness." 2 Peter 1:3, TPT

Since God has good plans for you and has already given you what you need, how can you change your thinking about your current situation?

_____

_____

_____

_____

What can you ask God to help you with? Write out a prayer here regarding how He can help you. When it comes to pass, share with someone what God has done for you.

_____

_____

_____

_____

What is one life lesson you can take away from what you've learned in this section? How will you apply it in your life right now?

_____

_____

_____

_____

_____

_____

_____

_____

_____

_____

_____

_____

_____

Closing the Door to Deception

"You must learn to believe the truth of God's Word over the facts of your circumstances." – Anonymous

Janet believed lies about herself which created an "image" for her to be considered "easy prey." People who wanted to take advantage of her took whatever they wanted not realizing her vulnerability and fear.

At the root of it, her insecurity created a mental stronghold of deception reinforcing the lies she believed about herself. Lies like *no one loves me, giving my body away demonstrates love, bad attention is better than no attention,* and *if I act and dress like everyone else, I'll be accepted.*

Here's the even worse part, we don't just believe lies about ourselves, we believe lies about God. Lies like, *He rejects me because I'm bad, I have to earn His love, or He will never give me another chance.*

In order to be free from deception, we need to replace the lies we've believed with the truth of God's Word. Then settle our heart on God's goodness, mercy, and lovingkindness towards us.

All deception and lies come straight from the devil. Read here what Jesus had to say about it;

"...He's been a murderer right from the start! He never stood with the One who is the true Prince [Jesus], for he's full of nothing but lies—lying is his native tongue. He is a master of deception and the father of lies!" John 8:44, TPT

The devil is a destroyer and he uses everything in your life to bring destruction. He attacks your identity because he hates the image of God. Then he uses every person who will cooperate with him to reinforce your feelings of being unloved, unaccepted, and unprotected. His intent is to keep you far away from your Heavenly Father and your Savior and Lord, Jesus Christ. But God loves you so much, He will have none of it. This is why He sent His Son Jesus to die for you and rescue you from the hand of the devil.

"Stay alert! Watch out for your great enemy, the devil. He prowls around like a roaring lion, looking for someone to devour. Stand firm against him and be strong in your faith." 1 Peter 5:8 & 9a

What are some of the lies you are believing about yourself right now?

_____

_____

_____

_____

Pray this;

> *Father forgive me for believing lies about myself. Today I close the door I opened to deception by allowing lies to take root in my heart. Holy Spirit help me to dig out those lies and replace them with God's truth. From this moment on I resist the father of lies and surrender my life to You. Take hold of me, mold and shape me into the person You created me to be, in Jesus' name. Amen.*

How do we replace lies with truth? We must take captive the thoughts we recognize as lies and intentionally replace them with what the Word says about who we are.

Here are a few examples:

- *I am worthless.* No, my worth is far above rubies, I am precious and priceless (Proverbs 31:10b).
- *I am unloved.* No, God has loved me with an everlasting love; therefore, with lovingkindness He has drawn me (Jeremiah 31:3).

37

- *I am not accepted.* No, God made me accepted in the beloved, I am His child (Ephesians 1:6).

Prayer is a powerful key. We have a Helper, the Holy Spirit, who Jesus said is the Spirit of Truth. Jesus went on to say that our Helper would lead and guide us into ALL TRUTH (John 16:13).

We need only ask the Holy Spirit for help with identifying lies and revealing truth to replace those lies. Let's pray;

> *Holy Spirit, help me replace the lies I have believed with the truth of God's Word. I ask in Jesus name. Amen.*

Now pay attention to your thoughts and what seem like promptings or stirrings in your heart or belly. The Holy Spirit will lead you. Pray often and keep your heart tender and receptive to Him. Acknowledge the lies He reveals, repent for each, and ask Him to fill you with truth.

Now declare this three times with me right now.

> *I close the door to deception NOW in Jesus' name!*

What is one life lesson you can take away from what you've learned in this section? How will you apply it in your life right now?

Additional Notes

Perfect Love

"...casts out ALL fear." – 1 John 4:18

Only the love of God can and will be perfect. God's love is called, *agape*, meaning selfless, sacrificial, and unconditional. It is not possible to measure God's love because it is unending. He doesn't base His love on your performance good or bad, His love IS, it just IS.

The word *lavish* comes to mind when I think about the love of God; extravagant, rich, luxurious, and generous. This is the true love our hearts long for. We keep seeking the love of God from others until we find it from the One who came to give us love in the beginning.

This is what God desires for every man, woman, and child that we grow up in His love, become strong adults and parents in His love, then teach their children about the love of God.

If the father of Janet's first child had the love of God, he would have never abused her. If her mother and father had the love of God, they would have never abandoned her. If her sisters and caregiver had the love of God, they would have supported her and cheered her on in her success. But they didn't so love got twisted.

Twisted love produces twisted people. Only Jesus can untwist a perverted love and heal our hurts, wounds, pain, disappointment, anger, shame, guilt, etc. His love relentlessly chases us, until we relent to Him. When we hear about and feel His perfect love, we melt completely into His arms. We are finally home. The one thing we longed for our whole life has finally been received.

Are there areas of your life where the love you give and receive from others is still twisted? Name those situations here.

_____

_____

_____

_____

Read and commit this verse to memory;

*"For **God loved** the world so much that **he gave** his one and only Son, so that everyone who believes in him will not perish but have eternal life." John 3:16*

God's love is not just meant to be received but given. The Hebrew word for love, *ahava*, means to give. God loves, He gives just like the verse above demonstrates. His love is unfailing. Since we are the recipient of His love, we are to give it to others as well.

What does unconditional love look like in your life? How would you demonstrate it to others?

_____

_____

_____

_____

Consider these characteristics of agape love;

- Patient, kind, thoughtful
- Not jealous or envious
- Doesn't brag, isn't proud or arrogant
- Not rude, self-seeking, overly sensitive, or easily angered
- Doesn't take or keep an account of suffered wrongs
- Rejoices when right and truth prevail
- Bears all things, believes the best in every circumstance
- Remains faithful to God in difficult times
- Doesn't allow love to fail, fade away, or come to an end

One of the most beautiful parts of Janet's story is that she loved despite the abuse, neglect, rejection and pain she received and felt.

How can you begin to extend God's love to those who have done these same things to you?

Take little steps and ask God to help you through the Holy Spirit. You will overcome as you do.

What is one life lesson you can take away from what you've learned in this section? How will you apply it in your life right now?

Additional Notes

God is in the Whirlwind

"Our mess is the canvas on which God paints His story of redemption." — *Louie Giglio*

Sometimes we make a mess in our life; a great big ugly mess. The mess may have been started by others, but it becomes our mess when we choose to remain a party to it.

Like Janet who lived out of her abuse and the lies she believed about herself, our mess can bring a sense of normalcy if it is all we have ever known. As distorted as this is, it is not a place too hard for God to reach. In fact, God lives there with everyone who is trapped in their distorted, destructive ways.

God is in the whirlwind of your life. He's not there to stand by with folded arms. He's there waiting for one cry, one call, one opening for Him to rush in and rescue you.

In the middle of Janet's whirlwind, God was reaching out to her hoping and trying to get her to relent to Him. But like she pointed out, her surrender meant the loss of control and she wasn't ready to *let go.*

The more we fight for control, the more we spin out-of-control. Right now, is the best time to surrender. When you let go and allow God to have control, then He will step in to defend you, deliver you, provide a way of escape and safe landing place for you. But first, you must loosen that tight grip.

Write down the people and things you need to surrender to God.

_____

_____

_____

_____

Pray this;

Father, I surrender my life, every person and circumstance that I am trying to control to You. Take hold Father, take control of my life. Help me to walk in peace as I release all to You. Holy Spirit teach me and lead me in all truth. Help me to recognize and repent every time I try to control anything or anyone. Give me a quiet, peaceful spirit. In Jesus name I pray. Amen!

What are some of the situations in your life where you need God to step in, defend and deliver you?

_____

_____

_____

_____

Read these verses;

> *"The Lord himself will fight for you. Just stay calm."*
> *Exodus 14:14*

> *"But the Lord has been my defense, and my God the rock of my refuge." Psalm 94:22*

> *He shall call upon Me, and I will answer him; I will be with him in trouble; I will deliver him and honor him. With long life I will satisfy him, And show him My salvation." Psalm 91:15—16*

> *"Rest in the LORD and wait patiently for Him; Do not fret because of him who prospers in his way, Because of the man who carries out wicked schemes." Psalm 37:7*

What happens when you make a mess? Know this, God is not mad at you, He loves you and wants to deliver you from your own mistakes, poor decisions, addictions, abuses, and destruction. He is merciful and kind, He does not tell you "you made your bed now lie in it." He is ready, willing, and able to deliver you right now.

Read these verses and meditate on them until you believe it with every fiber of your being.

"Then call on me when you are in trouble, and I will rescue you, and you will give me glory." Psalm 50:15

"In my distress I called upon the LORD and I cried to my God for help. From His temple He heard my voice, and my cry for His help reached His ears." Psalm 18:6

"Call on My name and I will answer you and show you great and mighty things you do not know." Jeremiah 33:3

How can you call on the Lord today?

_____

_____

_____

_____

What is one life lesson you can take away from what you've learned in this section? How will you apply it in your life right now?

_____

_____

Additional Notes

Standing Firm

Confused people often do the opposite of what is required to find clarity and wholeness. In Janet's case, she ran away when relationships got bad and old cycles started repeating again.

While leaving an abusive situation is good, if we don't have the support system of people who love Jesus and walk in truth, we end up back in old cycles repeatedly as Janet did for so many years.

Something had to change, but Janet had not yet made the connection. Like the Samaritan woman at the well, she writes about did the moment she encountered her Messiah. She made the connection, her life changed right then. Her purpose unfolded too!

The cycle must be interrupted, to be changed.

Are there destructive or unhealthy cycles in your life right now? Briefly identify them here.

_____

_____

_____

_____

To break cycles we must change people, places, and things. *Relationships* must end, we can't return to familiar *places*, and we must do whatever is necessary to be delivered from the *things* (drugs, alcohol, pornography, abuse of any kind) that destroy our life.

Read this verse;

> *"Do not be deceived: "Bad company ruins good morals."*
> *Wake up from your drunken stupor, as is right, and do not*
> *go on sinning." 1 Corinthians 15:33*

Darkness prevents us from seeing the reality of what is going on around us. While life spins out-of-control in the repeating cycles, we don't realize we hold the key to our own deliverance.

The cycle is like a hamster running on a wheel, as long as he runs the wheel spins. The only way to stop the spinning is for *the hamster to get off the wheel.*

Corrie Ten Boom once said, " *The first step on the way to victory is to recognize the enemy.*" We have two enemies; first our "self," then everyone else along with the devil who wants to destroy us. Here's the good news you have control over one thing, your choices.

Check this verse out;

> *"Rise from the dust, O Jerusalem. Sit in a place of honor. Remove the chains of slavery from your neck, O captive daughter of Zion." Isaiah 52:2*

Notice God's word to His daughter here. She has to rise up, she has to shake the dust off her feet. She has to make the choice to leave her slavery and go with God where she is honored.

How can you end the cycles you shared earlier?

_____

_____

_____

_____

Name a person who will support you bringing an end to a destruction or unhealthy cycle in your life.

_____

_____

_____

_____

Make a plan for ending the cycle and reaching out to a person who will support you as you make the changes necessary.

Let's pray;

Father God, You are good, You have good plans, You have peace in store. Help me. Strengthen me. As I have relinquished control, now I ask you to be with me as I make the changes necessary to end destructive and unhealthy cycles and to bring wholeness to my life. Make a way of escape for me to leave and provide a safe landing place, full of nurturing people who love You. In Jesus' name I pray, amen!

What is one life lesson you can take away from what you've learned in this section? How will you apply it in your life right now?

_____

_____

_____

_____

_____

_____

_____

_____

_____

_____

_____

Heaven's Victory

"God's ability to clean things up is infinitely greater
than our ability to mess things up." – Tullian Tchividjian
(Billy Graham's Grandson)

When one sinner finds salvation all of Heaven rejoices. Why? Because it's a great victory for the Kingdom of God. You. Your life. Your future is more valuable to God than you can imagine. His plans are infinitely greater.

As hard and fast as Janet ran away from the "Jesus freaks," religious people, and Christians, God relentlessly pursued her. He chases after rebels, He refuses to even bruise a broken reed. He is at work when everything seems to be crumbling around us.

This is why you simply *must* give your life to Jesus. Don't just pray a simple prayer and live life as if nothing happened. When you give your heart, your mind, your body to Jesus *everything* changes.

Does this mean everything and everyone including you will be perfect? No! It means that now He has control, He has possession, His plans will come to pass. All you need to do is surrender daily.

Paul wrote this beautifully to show believers exactly what their life should look like, read this;

"So dear brothers and sisters, I plead with you to give your bodies to God because of all he has done for you. Let them be a living and holy sacrifice—the kind he will find acceptable. This is truly the way to worship him. Don't copy the behavior and customs of this world, but let God transform you into a new person by changing the way you think. Then you will learn to know God's will for you, which is good and pleasing and perfect." Romans 12:1 & 2

When we give our life to Jesus everything changes. The Holy Spirit takes up residence in our heart and the transformation begins as God molds and shapes us into the person He created us to be. Our part? Keep surrendering and loving Him.

We surrender by giving our bodies (and soul; mind will and emotions) to Him.

What areas of your life; thinking, speaking, acting – can you surrender further to Him today?

_____

_____

_____

_____

Surrender is a life-long process, so don't ever think you have arrived. There's always more to give over to God.

We prove we love Jesus by keeping His commands. The Passion Translation puts this so beautifully;

"Loving Me empowers you to obey My commands." John 14:15

Loving Jesus and Father releases a grace that empowers or gives us the ability to do what we cannot do in our own strength. Try as we might to stop doing anything we fail and fail again. But acknowledging your love for God and Savior, then asking for help to overcome, starts a process of deliverance, healing, and ultimate wholeness as the Holy Spirit transforms your life.

What areas of your life are still in disobedience to the Lord?

_____

_____

_____

_____

Make this declaration with me;

I surrender ALL! Lift your hands and say again – I surrender
ALL! All to Jesus I surrender, I surrender ALL!

Stay on His path, walk with Him and all will be restored.

What is one life lesson you can take away from what you've learned in this section? How will you apply it in your life right now?

_____

_____

_____

_____

_____

_____

_____

_____

_____

_____

Additional Notes

Authenticity

"Authentic Christianity is a supernatural walk with a living, dynamic, communicating God." — Bill Hybels

Once you have experienced the real, authentic love and truth of God, you begin to see the false. You start to recognize the things and people that are contrary to Christ. Often the challenge of recognizing the counterfeits is determined by the depth of our roots in the foundations of Christ. Roots grow deeper as we grow in Him through prayer, His Word, and fellowship with Christians who are thriving and growing.

New Christians question themselves and override the Holy Spirit because they don't yet have confidence in their relationship with God. He is a dynamic communicator and like Janet in those moments when she heard Him clearly, He will speak to you.

Also, people new to faith in Christ don't realize there are "wolves in sheep's clothing" like Janet's new Christian friends told her. Who would think such a thing! When Christ is new, and love is real, the thought of a "Christian" lying, manipulating, controlling, and abusing couldn't be possible. As unfortunate as it is, there are many who masquerade as Christians. Jesus said we will know them by their fruit (Matthew 7:15—20).

Fruit is their actions. Do they live like Christ, treat people like Christ, love like Christ, etc.? We are not to judge, but we are to separate ourselves from them, pray for them and love them as God loves them.

Actions always speak louder than words. So, test the words of people by watching to see if their actions line up with what they are saying.

Have you ever overridden an inner voice or feeling that seemed to say, "don't do it"? If so, what were the results of going ahead even after knowing in your heart you shouldn't?

It's okay we've all done it. But this life in Christ is all about growing and becoming more mature in your walk with Him.

Don't ever be afraid to say "No." This one word is the most liberating word in any language. No! And it's okay to say no. You have to know your boundaries and when you don't want to do something, don't do it anyway. When you do you are not honoring your own boundaries. This is where regret, shame, guilt, and condemnation are born. When the Bible says,

> *"There is therefore now no condemnation to them which are in Christ Jesus, who walk not after the flesh, but after the Spirit."* Romans 8:1

You are not condemned for overriding the Holy Spirit. You get to try again. Make sure you are doing the work in your heart to be real, authentic, and confident in what and Who you know. Then the next time a counterfeit wants to lead you astray, you will be ready to respond the right way.

Watch for caution lights and stop signs! These are spiritual direction markers that we feel in our belly; a feeling of yuck, trepidation, or even a full-on strong sense of *NO!*

Practice what you will do next time you want to say no but are afraid to. Write a scenario here.

_____

_____

_____

_____

Write out what you believe being a Christian looks like.

_____

_____

_____

_____

Christianity is all about relationship. This is why the enemy tries to pervert our relationships with our parents, family, friends, sibling, spouses and children.

Until we get our relationship with our heavenly Father in right fellowship, we will never be able to have an authentic relationship based in Christ with anyone else. It is vital that we grow in our knowledge of God, His character, His unfailing love. As we grow in Him, we will be strong, confident, and gentle in all that we say and do.

How can you give more of your heart and mind to Him today?

_____

_____

_____

_____

Make this your daily pursuit and your life will be a beautiful tapestry of His love.

What is one life lesson you can take away from what you've learned in this section? How will you apply it in your life right now?

The Way Maker

"God will go before you and make the
crooked places straight."– Isaiah 45:2

God was with Janet before she was ever in her mother's womb.
He wrote her days before the foundation of the world. He knew her
and loved her. His plans for her were good, but she would have to
choose Him and His plan.

Read these verses;

> *"I knew you before I formed you in your mother's*
> *womb..." Jeremiah 1:5, NLT*
>
> *"You saw me before I was born. Every day of my life was*
> *recorded in your book. Every moment was laid out before a*
> *single day had passed." Psalm 139:16*
>
> *"Even as he chose us in him before the foundation of the*
> *world, that we should be holy and blameless before him."*
> *Ephesians 1:4*

It took many years for her to come to this realization, but step-
by-step God walked with her through everything making her path

straighter and straighter. All the while, moving her closer and closer to the purpose He had for her life.

As she became more acquainted with what it looked like to live an authentic Christian lifestyle, she rejected the thoughts, behaviors, and relationships that did not honor Jesus. She was being transformed in her heart and mind. This made the difference God desired, so He opened doors to take her into her calling.

God is so good this way. He is the Great Way Maker, nothing is too hard and no one is too far gone for Him.

What are some of the areas of your life right now that need transformation so that you can be more Christ-like?

_____

_____

_____

_____

How can you begin to choose a lifestyle in those areas that will honor Christ?

_____

_____

_____

_____

Read this verse;

> *"Put on your new nature and be renewed as you learn to know your Creator and become like him."* Colossians 3:10

When you read about Jesus' life in The Gospel of John and how He loved and treated people, you can begin to pattern your life after His. Also, surrounding yourself with people who love and follow Jesus will help you learn how to live this "new" life in Him.

As you continue to learn about Him, you will watch God transform your life, your relationships, even your job. He wants to be your sole source for everything in your life. Read this verse;

> *"To the fatherless he is a father. To the widow he is a champion friend. To the lonely he gives a family. To the prisoners he leads into prosperity until they sing for joy. This is our Holy God in his Holy Place!"* Psalm 68:5—6, TPT

How can you look to God more as your Source and Provider in all things?

_____

_____

_____

_____

Let's pray;

> *Father, I thank You that You have known me and loved me before I was alive. Thank You for never giving up on me and for delivering me from bad decisions and relationships. I give myself to You and I open my heart to allow You to transform my life. You are my Provider and You are enough for me. I love You and I will walk with You all the days of my life. In Jesus' name, Amen!*

What is one life lesson you can take away from what you've learned in this section? How will you apply it in your life right now?

_____

_____

_____

_____

Additional Notes

The Highway Leads to Wholeness

"God's goal for you is wholeness."— Max Lucado

As Janet continued to walk in the ways of God, whether she knew it or not at the time she was walking on the "great road" mentioned by the Prophet Isaiah (35:8). A spiritual road built through a once deserted land. I like to call this a road that goes up to God.

The longer we walk this road called the "Highway to Holiness" (Isaiah 35:8), the more we become like Christ in character and conduct. There's something else that happens as we walk this road, we become whole. Completely delivered, healed and restored to the fullness of what God created us to be—spirit, soul, and body. This includes our mental and emotional state.

Think of this road as one we should never turn around on. We can if we want to, but if we do, we are turning our attention away from our Father. We could even start walking the other way on this road, completely turning our back on Him. Don't do it. Keep your face turned toward Him and keep walking to Him.

In Christ, we must learn to always look forward. Life is never easy in this fallen world, everyone has wounds whether self-inflicted by wrong choices or others-inflicted by those who abuse and take advantage of us. Either way, we must forgive and move forward.

As Janet did, she found herself in a foreign country helping other women overcome abuse. As she continued in her pursuit of God and helping others with her passion to see them free, God brought a wonderful man into her life who loved Jesus and loves her as Christ loves the Church.

Leading up to that moment she never looked back, she never turned around, no matter the setbacks that would come she continued moving forward with God.

Read this verse;

> "I admit that I haven't yet acquired the absolute fullness that I'm pursuing, but I run with passion into his abundance so that I may reach the purpose that Jesus Christ has called me to fulfill and wants me to discover. I don't depend on my own strength to accomplish this; however, I do have one compelling focus: I forget all of the past as I fasten my heart to the future instead. I run straight for the divine invitation of reaching the heavenly goal and gaining the victory-prize through the anointing of Jesus." Philippians 3:12—14, TPT

"One compelling focus" is key. Let everything in your life be viewed through that focus; God, Jesus, and Heaven. Anything or anyone that gets in the way of this focus is a distraction that will either keep you from growing in Christ or take you in the wrong way. So, remove the distractions from your life.

What are some of the distractions in your life right now?

_____

_____

_____

_____

How can you remove them?

_____

_____

_____

_____

If you are too easily distracted perhaps you need a season of being surrounded only by people who will not pull you away from Jesus. There's great benefit in this. Read these verses and memorize them;

"So above all, constantly chase after the realm of God's kingdom and the righteousness that proceeds from him. Then all these less important things will be given to you abundantly." Matthew 6:33, TPT

"Make God the utmost delight and pleasure of your life, and he will provide for you what you desire the most." Psalm 37:4, TPT

What are some of the desires of your heart?

_____

_____

_____

_____

Love God, seek God, walk with God, listen to Him, and out of your love for Him, desire to please Him above all else. Then, you are headed in the right direction, and He will be able to transform and restore you completely as you walk the "great road"—the Highway to Wholeness.

What is one life lesson you can take away from what you've learned in this section? How will you apply it in your life right now?

Additional Notes

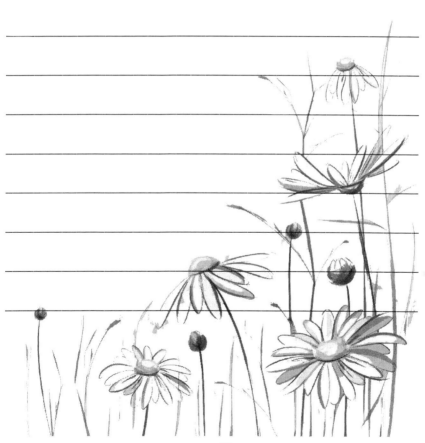

I Need Help Now

National Domestic Violence Hotline: 1-800-799-SAFE (7233)

National Suicide Prevention Lifeline: 1-800-273-TALK (8255)

About the Author

While Charlana Kelly is an accomplished entrepreneur, author, publisher, international Bible teacher, Radio & TV host, and a minister for more than twenty years, she is also a survivor of abuse.

Born to parents who did not want her; a mother who could not afford a fifth child and a father who urged his wife to abort the baby, Charlana grew up thinking she was unwanted and unworthy of love.

Adopted by loving and blessed parents she again felt rejected by her father because of his own abuse as a child. He didn't know how to love, so he used money to manipulate.

Lost, confused, and desperate in her heart she turned to drugs, alcohol, and inappropriate sexual relationships to find love and acceptance. All led to an incurable wound, and eventually to physical abuse by her first husband who nearly killed her before she could extricate herself by disappearing in the night.

Charlana gave her heart to Jesus as a child, loved the Lord, and wanted to serve Him. Through her pain, God grabbed hold of her again in her early twenties and began to change her desires. He sent an amazing man into her life, who Charlana didn't trust at first bracing herself for the rejection to come. It never came. Now 35 years later their love for each other and the Lord continues to grow deeper.

Charlana is the President of Speak Truth Media Group. Author of numerous books and educational programs. Host of the TV program *Engage for Influence* on Grace TV. You can connect with Charlana and obtain free resources at www.charlanakelly.org.

Connect

Purchase Janet's Book

"*Overcoming Abuse God's Way Rags to Riches*" at the following online book retailers:

www.christianbook.com

www.amazon.com

www.barnesandnoble.com

Connect with Janet and Overcoming Abuse God's Way on the Web and through Social Media

Website: www.overcomingabusegodsway.com

Facebook: Overcoming Abuse God's Way

Overcoming Abuse God's Way Radio Program

Twitter: Overcoming Abuse @OCAGW

Email: globalgogirl@gmail.com

Mobile: 901-605-8087

34681945R00054

Made in the USA
Middletown, DE
31 January 2019